Trost, Lucille Wood
    Biography of a cottontail

BIOGRAPHY OF A COTTONTAIL

About the Book

Everyone knows what a cottontail looks like, but its life in the wild may not be as familiar. Lucille Trost has given us a fascinating account of the first year in the life of Sylvi, a female cottontail. We follow Sylvi from her first days as a baby making timid explorations away from the nest, through her struggle against predators and the harsh winter elements, to having her own babies in the warm spring woodland.

BIOGRAPHY OF A
COTTONTAIL

by LUCILLE TROST

illustrated by LYDIA ROSIER

G.P. Putnam's Sons
New York

To my Mother, Grandmother and Sister
and the many cottontails we all knew

Copyright © 1971 by Lucille Trost
Illustrations copyright © 1971 by Lydia Rosier

All rights reserved. Published simultaneously in
Canada by Longmans Canada Limited, Toronto.

Library of Congress Catalog Card Number: 77-147279

PRINTED IN THE UNITED STATES OF AMERICA
07210

BIOGRAPHY OF A COTTONTAIL

When Sylvi* was born, she could neither see nor hear. She weighed only an ounce. Her hairless skin glowed a bright pink, and her ears were wrinkled and tiny. She did not look at all like her soft brownish cottontail rabbit mother.

Sylvi had four brothers that looked almost exactly like her. All of them were born in early May in the deep grass of an apple orchard. The mother rabbit cleaned and nursed the babies.

Sylvilagus is the name scientists call cottontails.

One by one she carried them to the hole she had dug and lined with bits of fur from her chest. When the last baby had been cared for, the mother rabbit covered the nest with a mat of leaves and fur. Then she hopped away. The nest was hidden. A hungry fox had walked by only a few feet away and not seen it.

At first the world of the baby cottontails was quiet and dark. The soft fur in the nest kept them warm and dry. They spent most of the time sleeping. Sylvi only squeaked softly or pushed herself about on her stomach when she was hungry. The mother rabbit was feeding nearby hidden in the tall grass. Several times each night she came to the nest and spread her body over it. Sylvi reached up to suck the sweet good milk until she was full. Then she slept.

Sylvi grew quickly. Only one hour after birth, the bright pink of her skin had begun to fade. The next day, her back and sides were covered with hair. By the end of the week, Sylvi had a good coat of fur and had begun to look like her mother.

On the sixth day after she was born, an exciting change happened to Sylvi and her brothers. She began to see. A slit appeared between her once-sealed eyelids. It slowly widened as the hours passed, but it was a day and a half before her eyes were completely open. During this same time, the wax plugs dissolved from her ears and she could hear.

When Sylvi could see and hear, she began to be more curious. She did not sleep so much. She and her brothers were restless. They squirmed about in the nest.

One day when Sylvi was about two weeks old, a crow flew to the ground beside the nest. He began to peck at the covering. Sylvi and her brothers squealed loudly. The mother rabbit rushed from her hiding place directly at the crow and knocked him over. After he had flown away, she continued to hop about nearby for a while. Then she fixed the covering and hid again.

That night Sylvi squirmed through the mat of leaves and fur and left the nest for the first time. She moved very slowly and never went more than a few yards away. The woodland night was filled with new sights and sounds. She froze when the wind rattled an overhanging limb. Bits of leaves and twigs fell from the nest of a squirrel. There was the faraway call of a barred owl. It sounded almost like the barking of a dog.

The small rabbit's nose twitched rapidly. First she moved with short hops with her back legs together. Then she stepped foot by foot the way a nervous mouse might. That night none of her brothers joined her. After an hour, she went back to the nest. There she snuggled against their warm bodies.

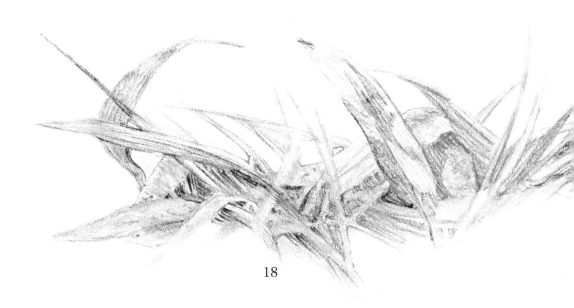

The next night all of the young rabbits began to explore. Sylvi was the bravest since she
had left the nest before. Her motions were fast-
er. She stopped less often, and she went farther
than she had the night before. After a while
she pushed her face into a clump of fresh young
grass and began to nibble. The taste was good.
From then on she drank less and less of her
mother's milk.

Before the sun rose, the babies all returned to the nest. But it was becoming very crowded. Each young rabbit already weighed almost four times its weight at birth.

For three more days Sylvi and her brothers lived in two places. During the day they slept in the nest. At night they came out to explore and to nibble on the tender grass and shrubs. Each baby had its own special hiding place, called a *form*. Sylvi had hollowed her spot in a patch of thick grass several yards from the nest. The back end of it was against the trunk of an apple tree. There she rested when she was not eating or exploring.

After the third night, the babies did not sleep in the nest, but they stayed close to it. They had learned to eat many different plants. Soon they did not drink their mother's milk at all.

One night as they played, a dark shape suddenly fell from the darkness. It was a great horned owl. It carried away one of Sylvi's brothers in its sharp claws. The cries of the little rabbit could be heard for a long time. When the owl came, Sylvi froze. Then she ran to her form and sat there a long while without moving.

When Sylvi began to feed again, she moved more quickly and stopped more often, but she did not seem to notice that her brother was gone. It was not long until the little cottontails played as before.

The mother rabbit no longer spent much time with the babies. Sometimes she fed close by, but she did not pay much attention to them. She had mated the same night that Sylvi and her brothers were born. Soon she would have new babies.

It was summer. The days were very hot. Sylvi and the other young rabbits moved away from one another and the nest. For a few weeks they returned to the grassy orchard to leap and play together. Soon they did not return at all. Sylvi and her brothers were six weeks old and almost grown. Now each would live alone.

Sylvi did not stay in the same place all summer. She moved constantly, exploring fifteen acres of hills, valleys, woodlands, and meadows. As she crouched near roads, she saw the bright lights of cars. Sometimes she met other young rabbits and played with them. Once she came near to the nest of a grown female. The big rabbit remained resting in her form. Young rabbits did not bother her. If Sylvi had been an adult she would have been driven away.

Sylvi ate constantly during the summer. Food was all about. She nibbled grass, sedge, clover, and goldenrod. She chewed the leaves and fruit of maple, apple, and wild cherry trees; blackberries, blueberries, strawberries, and grapes. Sylvi grew fat and healthy. When she was only five months old, she was full grown. Sylvi weighed two pounds and three ounces. Her brothers would never reach her size. Female cottontails are bigger than males.

As she moved about, Sylvi saw many new things. She also had many narrow escapes. She was chased by dogs and cats and foxes. It seemed that every meat-eating animal wanted cottontails for their dinners.

One evening Sylvi was nibbling clover. A dog came leaping from among the trees and began to chase her. Sylvi ran very fast, but the dog was gaining. Suddenly she jumped to the left. Then she continued running in a new direction.

The dog could not turn so quickly. Sylvi was farther ahead. When he gained on her, she jumped sideways again. At last Sylvi came close to a place of safety. She plunged into a thick blackberry patch. The dog was panting. He did not follow her.

On another evening Sylvi was eating sweet wild strawberries when a cat suddenly jumped out of the thicket. Sylvi usually ran from her enemies, but she could fight too. She twisted around and hit at the cat with her strong hind feet. Sylvi's toenails were sharp. Soon the cat screamed in pain and gave up. It ran away. Sylvi had only a few scratches.

Slowly fall came and the air grew cool. The leaves died. Sylvi stopped roaming. She found a pile of brush. With her sharp front teeth she cut pathways among the twigs. As the weather grew colder, Sylvi spent much more of her time hidden in the brush. Two younger rabbits had come to the brush pile also. They did not bother each other or Sylvi. Each cottontail had scratched out its own special form. Most of the time was spent resting or eating.

One night in late November the wind rose.
The air became very cold. As Sylvi was hopping
about nibbling upon the bark of a small willow
tree, the first sharp particles of snow began to
fall. Soon the world was full of whirling flakes.
Sylvi went back to the brush pile. All that night
she did not feed. She sat huddled in her form.
There she was protected. The snow piled up
over the branches. The brush heap soon was an
ice-covered house.

The winter was long and snowy and cold. There were many nights and many days when Sylvi did not leave her hideout to search for food. Her feet were not made to walk on top of soft snow. She would fall into the drifts and soon grow tired. One of the many other hungry animals might catch her.

When the weather was good, Sylvi left the brush pile. The many foods of summer were gone. Finding things to eat took most of her time. She nibbled the twigs and bark of many plants and trees. She ate the buds and needles of pines. She ate all the nourishing things she could find. Yet the food was not enough. Before spring came, Sylvi had lost four ounces of her normal weight. But for such a small loss, Sylvi was lucky. The two younger rabbits that had shared her brush pile were gone. One had been killed by a fox; the other had been eaten by an owl. Cottontails have only one chance in twenty to live a full year. It is rare when a rabbit lives to the old age of two years.

In late January, the male rabbits began to leave their winter hideouts to look for mates. One night as Sylvi nibbled upon some pine buds, a male rabbit came toward her. Sylvi stopped eating and watched him. Suddenly another male appeared. The two began to fight. They jumped about and slashed each other with sharp hind claws. At last one rabbit was beaten and hopped away. Sylvi mated with the male that remained. For several days, the two rabbits stayed together. They romped and played. Then instinctively Sylvi seemed to grow angry. She rushed at the male and drove him away. When she mated again, probably it would be with another rabbit. Sylvi would not remember her first mate.

About three weeks after she had mated, Sylvi started to act differently. She ate less and moved about more often. She seemed to be searching for something. At last she went to a low place near a stream and began to dig. She used her front paws as shovels. Quickly she scraped away the dirt. When she stopped, the hole was about five inches wide, six inches long, and four inches deep.

Sylvi hopped away. When she returned, her mouth was full of dried grass. She used it and bits of fur pulled from her chest and abdomen to line the nest.

When Sylvi had finished making the nest, it was morning. A flicker flew across the open space between two nearby trees. He began his tapping search for breakfast. A large gray squirrel chattered and scampered about on the ground.

Sylvi was tired from digging and lining the nest. She hopped to her hidden spot beneath some overhanging shrubs. There she sat all day dozing nervously as her swollen sides moved.

At dusk Sylvi came again from her shelter. For the first few hours she hopped about the orchard. She fed upon the tender young buds that had pushed through the earth. Later she went to the nest and examined it. All seemed well, so she returned to her form to rest another day.

On the third evening, Sylvi gave birth to five babies. They were born on the ground about twenty feet from the nest, but Sylvi did not seem worried. She cleaned the babies and nursed them. Then one by one she carried them to the nest. Finally she covered the depression with a mat of leaves and fur. Instead of sitting on the nest, she remained hidden nearby. There she spent a lot of time cleaning herself.

During the night a male rabbit came to Sylvi. Sylvi mated again. Female rabbits almost always mate the night after they have given birth. The male rabbit stayed nearby for a few days. As before, Sylvi at last drove him away.

When the babies were three days old, a bad storm came. The sky grew black. It rained very hard and Sylvi huddled in her form. When it was over, she hurried to the nest. It was filled with water. The five babies were dead. But the mother cottontail did not seem upset. She hopped about the spot for a while, and then she went away.

A month later, again Sylvi built another nest for the babies about to be born. This time she chose a higher spot between two large clumps of grass. She dug and lined the cavity then returned to hide. But when she visited the hole the following night, something seemed wrong. The nest was disordered. She paused and twitched her nose rapidly. It had only been a field mouse, but Sylvi did not know this. Instinct drove her to leave the nest. Her new babies would have to be hidden in some other place.

Sylvi searched again in the darkness. She stopped by the hole of a badger. She explored a wheel depression from the farmer's apple-picking cart. Neither of these seemed to please her. At last Sylvi chose a place against the shelter of a tree trunk.

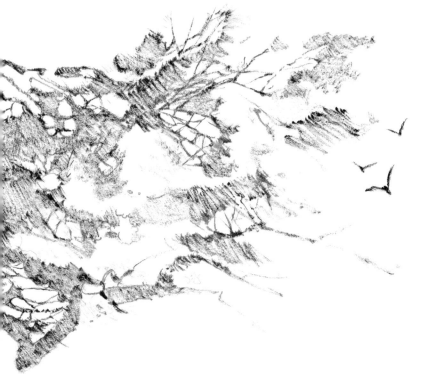

It was the middle of April. Spring was in the air again. By the time Sylvi was one year old she would give birth to her second litter in the warm growing woodland.

About the Author

Lucille Trost was born in New York State and holds degrees in zoology and biology from Pennsylvania State University and the University of Florida. She has done medical and biological research and has written several articles and a book on camping. Mrs. Trost lives with her husband and young son in Pocatello, Idaho, where recently she was one of several parents to help initiate an experimental elementary school. *Biography of a Cottontail* is her first book for young children.

About the Artist

Lydia Rosier was born in Switzerland and educated in the Netherlands. In the United States she studied at the Art Students League and the School of Visual Arts. She later worked as art director for a leading book publishing house and has painted portraits and landscapes for both institutions and private individuals. Miss Rosier has won several top honors and awards for her work and free-lances now exclusively, illustrating both adult and children's books.

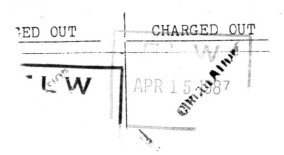